For Lucas & his Rex – M. G. L.

For Fay & Beata – D. B.

First published in 2020 by Scholastic Children's Books

a division of Scholastic Ltd

Euston House, 24 Eversholt Street, London NW1 1DB

London • New York • Toronto • Sydney • Auckland • Mexico City • New Delhi • Hong Kong

Text copyright © 2020 M. G. Leonard • Illustrations copyright © 2020 Duncan Beedie

Photos of male and female rhinoceros beetles © Bennytrapp / Adobe Stock 2019

PB ISBN 978 1407 19418 9

Printed in China

The moral rights of M. G. Leonard and Duncan Beedie have been asserted.

This product is made of FSC®-certified and other controlled material

FSC
MIX
Paper from responsible sources
FSC® C008047

10 9 8 7 6 5 4 3 2 1

M. G. LEONARD

REX
the Rhinoceros Beetle

Illustrated by
DUNCAN BEEDIE

SCHOLASTIC

Deep in the rainforest.
I spy two rhinoceros beetles.

"Hey, Rex, check out this banana!
Will you help me carry it
to the beetle tree?"

"I'll do my best, Buster. But it's very big. Where did you get it?"

"I rolled a boulder as big as a **baby elephant** against the banana plant and climbed it," says Buster.

"WOW! You are super strong," Rex says. "But how did you get the banana down?"

"I chopped it down with my horn," Buster replies. "My horn is as sharp as a **sword**."

"**Amazing!**" Rex says.

"I wish my horn could chop things."

"Then **a snake** slithered out of the plant, wanting to eat me!" Buster says.

"Oh no!" Rex gasps. "What did you do?"

"I rose up onto my back legs and opened my wings. The snake was **terrified**."

"You're a **hero**, Buster," Rex sighs. "I wish I were as brave as you."

Buster nods.
"Yes, I am VERY brave."

CRACK!

"What was that?"
Rex looks up.

"Buster! Where are you going?
Don't you want your banana back?"

"Want it back?"
Buster squeaks.
All six of his knees are knocking.

The monkey peers through the knotted root, licking his lips.

"Quick, Buster, use your **mighty strength!**" Rex says.

"Um, I'm not actually that strong," Buster whispers.
"I didn't roll a giant boulder."

"It's not," Buster wails.
"I found the banana on the ground."

Buster starts to cry.

"I can't even frighten wiggly worms!"

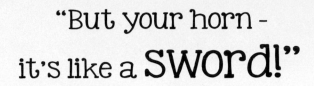

"But your horn - it's like a **SWORD!**"

"So scare the monkey away, like you did with that snake."

And suddenly, Rex realises that Buster is...

"Oh, Rex! We're going to get munched by a monkey!"

Buster blubbers.

The monkey reaches into the hole and grabs Buster.

"Help me, Rex! DO SOMETHING!"

"Oh no, you don't, monkey," Rex cries.
"No one eats my friends!"

He rises up onto his back legs,
points his horns at
the monkey and lets out
an almighty...

HISSSSSSSSS

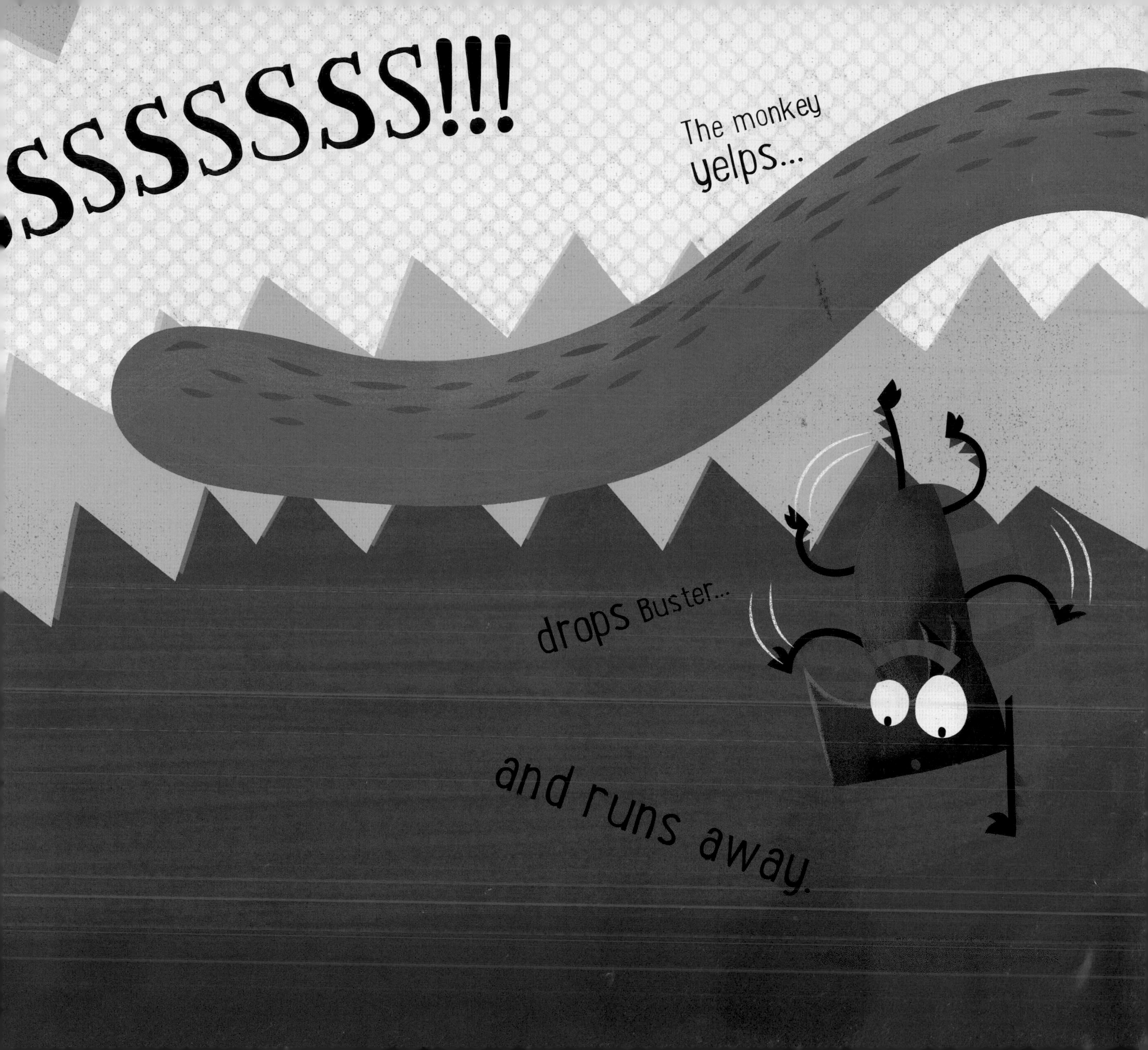

SSSSSSS!!!

The monkey yelps...

drops Buster...

and runs away.

"Rex! You scared the monkey away!"

"I did, didn't I?" Rex says with surprise. "But Buster, you shouldn't have **lied** about being strong."

"I'm sorry," Buster says. "I won't do it again."

Back at the beetle tree.
Buster tells everyone.

"Rex is a hero! You
should have seen him!
He saved my life!"

"How?" the beetles ask.

"He scared away a . . ."

"Wow! I could never
scare a giant gorilla.
Rex must be super
strong."

AMAZING RHINOCEROS BEETLE FACTS!

The beetle gets its name because it has a **horn** on its head like a **rhinoceros.**

Rhinoceros beetles can **fly.** Their horns are hollow and light.

Only **boy** rhinoceros beetles have horns.

Baby rhinoceros beetles are called larvae and eat rotting wood.

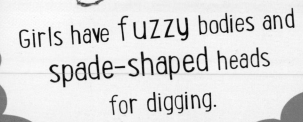

Girls have **fuzzy** bodies and **spade-shaped** heads for digging.

Rhinoceros beetles are

BIG.

Considering their size, rhino beetles are among the **strongest** creatures on the planet.

Rhinoceros beetles can't bite or sting or hurt you.

Rhinoceros beetles eat over-ripe fruit and tree sap.

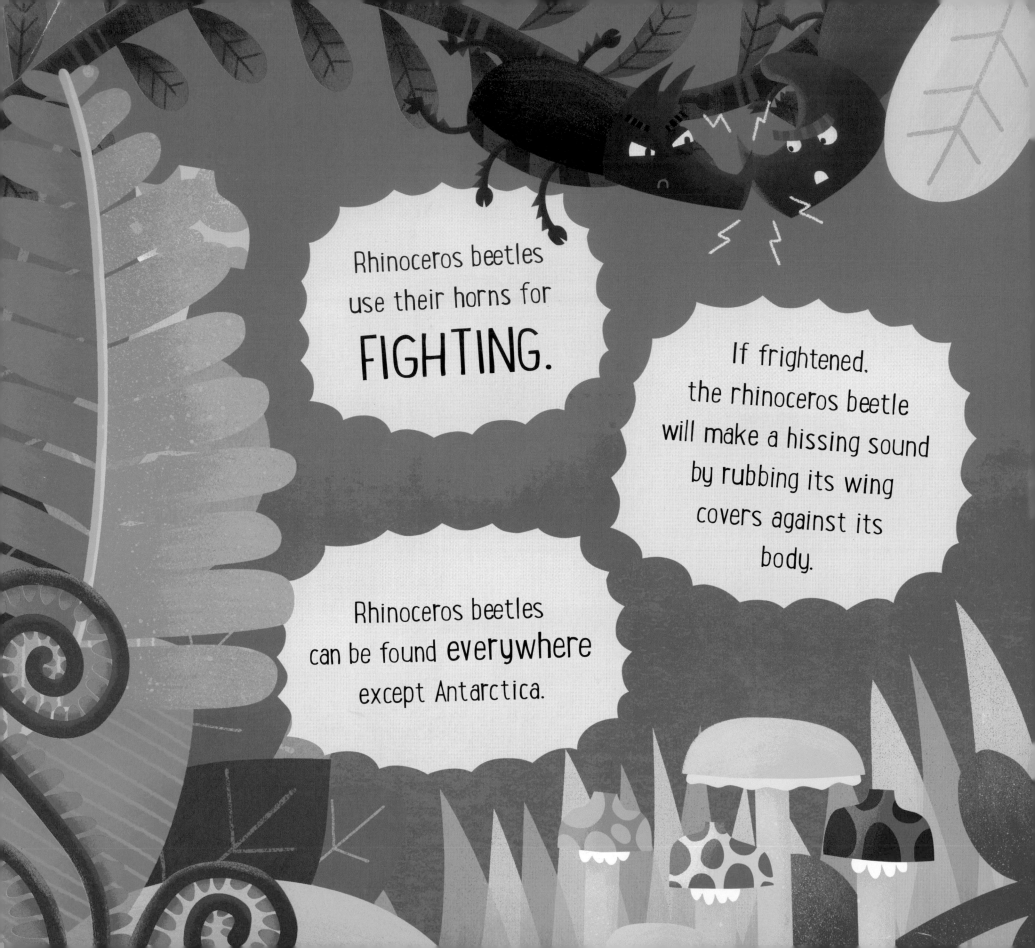

Rhinoceros beetles use their horns for **FIGHTING.**

If frightened, the rhinoceros beetle will make a hissing sound by rubbing its wing covers against its body.

Rhinoceros beetles can be found **everywhere** except Antarctica.

HOW PEOPLE CAN HELP BEETLES

(and other insects)

- Stop using pesticides
- Let a corner of your garden become overgrown
- Create a bug hotel
- Put a pond in your garden
- Build a log pile
- Turn all of the lights off at night
- Plant a mix of wildflowers